Thank you ...

... for buying this copy of

Andrew Brodie's **Best Handwriting for ages 7 - 11.**

The sheets can be photocopied onto paper, card or overhead projector transparencies. Please note that copies can only be made for use by the purchasing institution. Supplying copies to other schools, institutions or individuals breaches the copyright licence. Thank you for your help in this.

Andrew Brodie's **Best Handwriting for ages 7 - 11** includes:

... a complete handwriting policy for your school

... the correct way to hold the pen and the paper or book

... sitting comfortably and appropriately for writing

... the structure of individual letters

... correct techniques for joining letters

... capital letters and lower case letters

... punctuation marks and their use

... numerals and the pound sign

... writing informal and formal correspondence

... a complete programme of work to encourage

neat, legible, joined handwriting.

To find details of our other publications, please visit our website:

www.acblack.com

Developing a Programme of Work

To change and improve pupils' handwriting rapidly you will need to follow a course of regular daily practice for just a few weeks.

We recommend that handwriting practice should take place on a daily basis for approximately ten to fifteen minutes. This can take place outside the Literacy Hour.

Pupils should be given a copy of one or two of our practice sheets per session. They should also have a handwriting book to continue their practice if they complete the activities on the sheets. This book should be an ordinary exercise book, ruled with lines which are 8mm apart. Learning to position their writing correctly in relation to these lines is a crucial part of the handwriting improvement process.

Pupils make best progress with handwriting when they are shown exactly how to form the letters. We suggest that the teacher demonstrates the letter structure on a blackboard or whiteboard or by photocopying our Practice Sheets onto Overhead Projector Transparencies and drawing the letter shapes on them. Each short handwriting lesson should start with this brief demonstration of the letters and words to be covered within the session. The children should then work on the photocopied sheets independently, with the teacher circulating to check letter formation and to offer praise and support. It is important that the children follow exactly the letter formation shown on the sheets.

'Best Handwriting' includes a proposed School Handwriting Policy. In accordance with this policy, Sheets 1 to 37 can be used with Year 3 pupils, where not every letter is joined. We are suggesting that from Year 4 and above pupils should be taught a system of total joining: ie, except for the capital letters, every letter can be joined to the one which follows it within a word. With Years 4, 5 and 6, Sheets 1 to 37 are of great value in reminding pupils of letter structures, sizes and positions before moving on to total joining by using Sheets 38 onwards.

Many children really enjoy handwriting practice. They gain particular satisfaction by seeing their own writing transformed over a short period of time.

Contents

Handwriting at Reception Level

Establishing good writing habits at Reception level is extremely important.

We will ensure that each child holds the pencil comfortably and appropriately:

The pencil should be held between the thumb and first finger and should rest on the middle finger. It should be held at about 2 to 3 centimetres from the point.

We will provide 'chubby' pencils where appropriate. We will provide special pencil grips for those children who need them. We will consider the special requirements of left-handed children, ensuring that they hold their paper at an appropriate angle.

We will provide plenty of practice in using pencils, crayons and other writing implements to encourage children to gain confidence in drawing and in producing controlled lines.

We will encourage children to write each letter using controlled movements as shown in the letter formation guides below. Where appropriate with certain letters, we will introduce a 'tail' to encourage a style which will be easy to join in the future. We will check each child's writing as they work and record their progress on a class record sheet, indicating whether they can form each letter of the alphabet correctly.

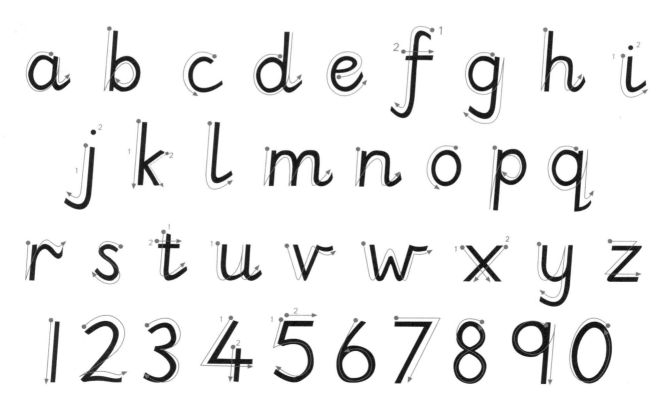

Handwriting at Year 1

We will further encourage the good handwriting habits developed in Reception.

We will ensure that each child holds the pencil comfortably and appropriately:

The pencil should be held between the thumb and first finger and should rest on the middle finger. It should be held at about 2 to 3 centimetres from the point.

We will provide 'chubby' pencils where appropriate. We will provide special pencil grips for those children who need them. We will consider the special requirements of left-handed children, ensuring that they hold their paper at an appropriate angle.

We will encourage children to write each letter as shown in the letter formation guides below. Where appropriate with certain letters, we will introduce a 'tail' so that the children will become accustomed to a style which will be easy to join in the future.

We will check each child's writing as they work and record their progress on a class record sheet, indicating with a tick whether they can form each letter of the alphabet correctly.

We will practise handwriting with the children alongside their spelling practice. We will encourage the use of tidy and well-formed writing in all independent work.

Handwriting at Year 2

We will continue to develop the handwriting patterns developed in Year 1.

We will ensure that each child holds the pencil comfortably and appropriately:

 The pencil should be held between the thumb and first finger and should rest on the middle finger.
It should be held at about 2 to 3 centimetres from the point.

We will provide special pencil grips for those children who need them. We will consider the special requirements of left-handed children, ensuring that they hold their paper at an appropriate angle.

We will encourage children to write each letter using controlled movements as shown in the letter formation guides for Year 1.

We will introduce the four basic joins:

…slope joins to letters without ascenders:

an en in do um

…bridge joins to letters without ascenders:

on ri vo wa fi

…slope joins to letters with ascenders:

al eb it mb uh

…bridge joins to letters with ascenders:

oh wh rl ot

We will check each child's writing as they work and record their progress on a class record sheet, indicating with a tick whether they can form each type of join correctly.

We will practise handwriting with the children alongside their spelling and phonic practice and we will encourage the use of tidy writing in all independent work.

Handwriting at Year 2 continued

At this stage we will not join from the following letters:

b g j k p q s x y z

six   bags   jelly

foxes   keys

pin   quiz   zoo

1 2 3 4 5 6 7 8 9 0

Handwriting at Year 3

We will ensure that each child holds the pencil comfortably and appropriately:

The pencil should be held between the thumb and first finger and should rest on the middle finger.
It should be held at about 2 to 3 centimetres from the point.

We will provide special pencil grips for those children who need them. We will consider the special requirements of left-handed children, ensuring that they hold their paper at an appropriate angle.

We will continue to develop the joins introduced in Year 2:

...slope joins to letters without ascenders: *an en in do um*

...bridge joins to letters without ascenders: *on ri vo wa fi*

...slope joins to letters with ascenders: *al eb it mb uh*

...bridge joins to letters with ascenders: *oh wh rl ot*

At this stage we will not join from the following letters: *b g j p q s x y z*

We will introduce the letter *k* as a joining letter, as shown here:

k   kettle

We will check each child's writing as they work and record their progress on a class record sheet, indicating with a tick whether they can form each type of join correctly.

We will use 8mm lined paper, encouraging children to write letters of consistent size, where most letters sit on the line and descenders pass through it. We will show how to leave an appropriate gap between words, of approximately the width of two letters.

We will practise handwriting with the children alongside their spelling and phonic practice and we will encourage the use of tidy writing in all independent work, while at the same time developing speed and fluency. We will introduce the correct formations of question marks, exclamation marks, commas and speech marks.

Handwriting at Year 4

We will continue the practice of joins developed in Years 2 and 3:

...slope joins to letters without ascenders: *an en in do um*

...bridge joins to letters without ascenders: *on ri vo wa fi*

...slope joins to letters with ascenders: *al eb it mb uh*

...bridge joins to letters with ascenders: *oh wh rl ot*

We will introduce joining from the following letters: *bg j p q s x y z*

... incorporating new forms of letters f and x:

... and resulting in a system of total joining:

fix six bags expert jelly quays zoo

Capital letters will remain unjoined.

Pupils will use joined writing for all writing, except for special projects or other aspects of presentation where different styles are required. For example, pupils may use printed script or capital letters for titles, headings, posters, etc.

We will teach the use of apostrophes to show possession and contraction and will show the pupils how to write apostrophes of appropriate shape, size and angle to fit well with their handwriting. We will revise the formation and use of punctuation marks, including commas, speech marks, question marks and exclamation marks.

We will encourage pupils to develop skills of writing quickly but legibly for notes and informal work. We will help pupils to realise that there are times when neat work is essential and other times when less formal writing is needed.

We will use 8mm lined paper or plain paper with an 8mm line guide, encouraging children to write letters of consistent size, where most letters sit on the line and descenders pass through it. We will show how to leave an appropriate gap between words, of approximately the width of two letters.

Handwriting at Years 5 and 6

We will continue the practice of joins developed in Year 4:

...slope joins to letters without ascenders: *an en in do um*

...bridge joins to letters without ascenders: *on ri vo wa fi*

...slope joins to letters with ascenders: *al eb it mb uh*

...bridge joins to letters with ascenders: *oh wh rl ot*

...including joins from the following letters: *b g j p q s x y z*

... incorporating these forms of letters f and x: *f x*

... and resulting in a system of total joining: *fix six bags expert jelly quays zoo*

Capital letters will remain unjoined.

Pupils will use joined writing for all writing, except for special projects or other aspects of presentation where different styles are required. For example, pupils may use printed script or capital letters for titles, headings, posters, etc.

We will revise the use of apostrophes to show possession and contraction and will remind the pupils how to write apostrophes of appropriate shape, size and angle to fit well with their handwriting. We will consider the formation and use of punctuation marks, including commas, speech marks, question marks, exclamation marks, colons, semi-colons, dashes and brackets. We will check that pupils can write numerals neatly and correctly, as learnt in previous years. We will ensure that pupils can write pound signs correctly:

1 2 3 4 5 6 7 8 9 0 £

We will encourage pupils to develop skills of writing quickly but legibly for notes and informal work. We will help pupils to realise that there are times when neat work is essential and other times when less formal writing is needed.

Individual Lower Case Letters at Key Stage 2:

Numerals, pound signs and question marks:

Formation of Capital Letters

© Andrew Brodie Publications   www.acblack.com

School Handwriting Policy

Special Requirements for Left-Handed People:

Left-handed people can experience greater difficulties than right-handed people with writing. However, with appropriate guidance, left-handed children can develop handwriting which is just as neat as that of their right-handed classmates.

The following advice should be given to left-handed children:

Take care not to press too hard when you are writing.

Try to use a pen with ink which flows easily.

Left-handed people have to 'push' the pen across the paper rather than 'pull' it as right-handed people do.
Free-flowing ink reduces the need to press hard, thus avoiding digging into the paper.

Hold your paper at an angle so that you can see what you have written.

Left-handed people often find that their hand covers their writing so that they cannot see what they have written.
It is thought that this can inhibit correct spelling.
Covering the writing with the hand can also cause smudging.

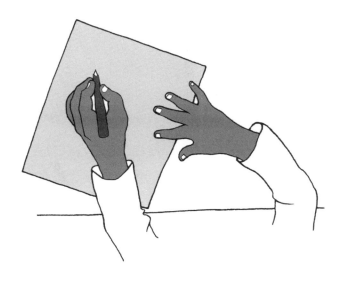

Rules for Good Handwriting

Make sure that your table or desk is not cluttered:

You cannot write well where you have piles of books, pens, pencil-cases or other odd items.

GIVE YOURSELF SPACE.

Sit where you have good light on your work.

Sit comfortably at your table,

so that you can see each letter as you write.

Hold your paper still.

Hold your pen near the point but

not so close that your fingers get inky.

Choose a pen which you like using:

Make sure it is not too thin or too fat.

Select a pen which 'feels right' in your hand.

Find a pen which allows ink to flow freely, so that you do not have to press hard on the paper.

Don't use a pen which makes blobs of ink.

If you are choosing a cartridge pen, make sure that the cartridges are easy to change.

Practice Sheet 1: Starting with letter c

It may seem strange but we are going to start by looking at the letter c.

Letter c makes a good starting point for several other letters of the alphabet.

Now try some for yourself:

Let's get smaller:

C C C

...and smaller:

c c c

Most exercise books and sheets of lined paper have line spacings of 8 millimetres:

You need to write your letters so that they sit on the bottom line and are about half as tall as the total space. We have drawn an extra faint line to help you:

c c c

c c c

c c c

Now try without the extra line. Make sure you keep the letters the same size:

c c c

We are now going to look at the letter o.
This starts in exactly the same place as a letter c.
Unlike the c it finishes in the same place as it started.

Now try some for yourself.
Make sure that each letter sits exactly on the line.

OOO

o o o

Now let's look at letter a. This is made in the same way as the c and the o. When you reach the finish point of the o, continue upwards by a small amount, then come down to the line and finish with a small sloping upstroke:

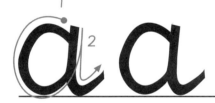

aaa

a a a

We are now going to try writing the word 'cocoa'. Don't try to join yet - that's coming soon. Do try to keep your letters on the bottom line and leave gaps between words.

cocoa cocoa cocoa

cocoa

Look again at letters c, o and a.
Letter d is very similar to the letter a but obviously the 'stick' is taller.
Because letter d is taller than the other letters we call it an **ascender**.

Now try some for yourself.
Make sure that each letter sits exactly on the line.

d d d

_d d d_

The letter g is made in a similar way to the c and the o.
Because letter g goes below the line we call it a descender.

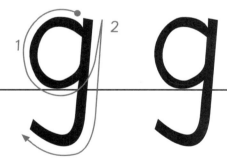

g g g

_g g g_

We have three new words to practise. The lines are shown as they would appear in most exercise books. Notice how high the d goes and how far below the line that the g goes.

cod

dog

good

Letter e is created using the same anticlockwise movement which we have used in all the letters so far, but we start this letter in a different place:

eee

eee

Letter q is similar to the letter g:

qqq

qqq

Letter s is formed by starting with our familiar anticlockwise movement then curling quickly round to a clockwise movement:

 S

Try copying this pattern of letters s and c. Make sure that the s is the height of the c.

SC SC

SC SC SC

Try writing the word 'case' several times:

case

Let's look at the word 'cocoa' in joined writing:

Look at the slope join which we use to join the letter c to the letter o,
then practise writing the joined 'co' yourself.

co

co

Now look at the bridge join from the letter o to the letter a,
then practise writing the joined 'oa' yourself.

oa

oa

Try writing the word 'cocoa' in joined writing.
Make sure that all the letters sit neatly on the line.

cocoa

cocoa

cocoa

cocoa

Practice Sheet 6: The First Joins

Look at the words 'cod' and 'dog'. Both of them have a slope join and a bridge join.

Practise writing the words 'cod' and 'dog' in joined writing.

cod

cod

dog

dog

Look carefully at the joins in the word 'code':

We normally write a
letter e like this: e

To join, we change it
to look like this: e

Try practising the word 'code'.

code

code

© Andrew Brodie Publications www.acblack.com

Practise the word 'cocoa' in joined writing:

cocoa

Now try the word in smaller writing. Follow these important rules:

Remember to keep all the letters exactly the same height.

Make sure that all the words sit neatly on the line.

Keep a clear gap between the words.

cocoa cocoa

cocoa

cocoa

Did you manage to keep your letters the right size even though the extra guideline was missing? Now try the words 'cod' and 'dog'.

cod dog

cod dog

cod dog

cod dog

Notice that we make sure that the tail of the g does not crash into the stick of the d.

When you practise the word 'code', remember that it has two different types of join: the **slope** from the c to the o, the **bridge** from the o to the d and the **slope** from the d to the e. Notice that this slope is at the same angle as the slope from the c to the o.

code

code code

code code

code code

code code

The formation of the letter s changes slightly when we make a join to it.
Look carefully at this word:

New shape s

Normal shape s

Practise writing the words 'odes' and 'codes' in joined writing.

odes

odes
codes
odes
codes

At this stage, we do not join from the letter g or the letter s.
Look at the words 'dogs' and 'seeds':

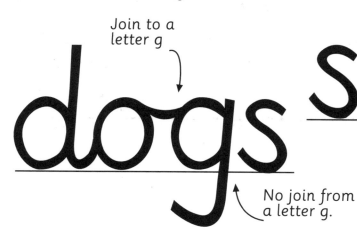

Join to a letter g

No join from a letter s.

Join to a letter s

No join from a letter g.

Practise writing the words 'dogs' and 'seeds' in joined writing.

dogs
seeds

Practice Sheet 9: No joins from s and g

Try writing the word 'gas' in joined writing. Remember not to join from the letter g.

gas

gas

gas

gas

Now try the word 'seeds'. Remember not to join from the letter s.

seeds

seeds

seeds

seeds

Practise each of the words below. Be careful with letter sizes.

as

cages

cogs

goose

codes

Now practise the words again, writing as quickly as you can. Are they still tidy?

as

cages

cogs

goose

codes

The letter l is the same height as the letter d but is formed differently.
For this letter we start at the top, draw down to the line, then finish with an upward slope ready to join to the next letter.
Practise writing the letter l in this large size:

Now try the letter l again using smaller writing.
Remember to keep all the letters the same height.

Now try the letter h. This is the same height as the letter l.
It is formed by drawing 'down, up and over'.

Now try the letter h again using smaller writing.
Remember to keep all the letters the same height.

Letter i is made in the same way as the letter l, but it is not as tall and it also has a dot.
Practise both sizes of the letter i.

You need to be very careful when joining to a tall letter like h or l. Look at the word 'ill'. At the end of the letter i we need to slope up to the starting point of the letter l, then draw down exactly along the same line:

We draw the dot on the letter i, after we have written the rest of the word.

Try writing the word 'hill' in joined writing. Slope up from the h to the i, from the i to the first l and from the first l to the second l.

hill hill

Notice how tall the letters h and l are compared to the letter i. Making sure that your letters are the correct height can make a huge difference to your handwriting.

hill hill hill
hill
hill

Here is a short phrase. Write it several times.
Try to make each phrase look better than the one before.

a high hill
a high hill

Practise each of the words below. Be careful with letter sizes.

halls
calls
called
cold

Practice Sheet 12: Joining to tall letters

You need to be very careful when joining to tall letters.
Let's look again at the join from a letter i to a letter l:

You have a choice:

You can flow from the letter i right up to the top of the letter l …

… or, if you find it easier, you can briefly take your pen off the paper at the end of the slope of the letter i, then draw the letter l so that it looks like it is joined to the letter i:

Practise the join from a letter i to a letter l.

il

Now let's look at joining from a letter o to a letter l. As you will remember, we normally use a bridge join from the top of a letter o to the next letter. When joining from letter o to a tall letter, we make a sloping join.

Practise these words:

oh so old

oil

hose

deal

each

© Andrew Brodie Publications   www.acblack.com

Practise joining a letter i to a letter l.
First try joining where you keep the pen flowing from the slope of the letter i right up to the starting point of the letter l:

il

il

Now try the method where you take your pen off at the end of the slope from the letter i, then draw the letter l to look like it's joined to the letter i:

il

il

Let's practise joining from a letter o to tall letters like l and h:

ol oh

Try writing this short phrase several times:

oh so old

These words give you practice in joining to tall letters:

eel

heel

chill

hail

dale

Letter n is very similar to letter h. It is formed by drawing 'down, up and over'.

Letter m is very similar to letter n. It is also formed by drawing 'down, up and over' but then the 'up and over' is repeated:

Now is a good time to remember letter sizes. Let's look at all the letters we've practised so far. They can be sorted into three groups:

... ordinary small letters: c o a e s i n m

... tall letters, called ascenders: d h l

... letters which go below the line, called descenders: g q

Now practise all the letters which we have used so far.

c o a d g e q s h i l m n

Try writing the word 'name' in joined writing.
Make sure that all the letters are exactly the same height,
fitting neatly between the lines provided.

name

name

name

Practise each of the words below. The ascender letter l should be taller than the small letters in the words. The smaller letters should all be exactly the same height. This time there are no extra lines to guide you. You will need to judge sizes carefully.

male

mail

lane

lemon

Look carefully again at a letter g. The **bowl** of the g should be sitting exactly on the line, as the other letters do. The **tail** of the g should go through the line.

game

Practise each of the words below.

game

song

dancing

singing

single

sand

coming

Letter r is formed in a similar way to a letter n by going 'down, up and over' but obviously we don't go right over. Look at these letters n and r:

Letter t is formed from the top like a letter l. It is not as tall as a letter l. We draw the cross-line on the t **after** we have finished the word we are writing. If there is a double t, we draw the line through both letters together.

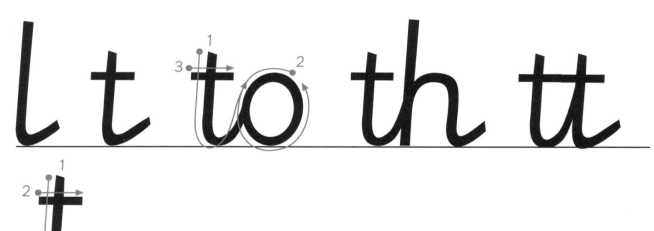

Practise the letter t.

t

to

Try writing the word 'right' in joined writing.
Draw the cross-line on the t last of all.

right

right

right

Practise each of the words below.

grill

goat

dart

start

These words contain a common letter pattern which has a letter t at the end:

light

night

might

tight

Practise each of the words below.

great

state

gate

Now try these words, writing as quickly as you can. Can you keep your writing tidy?

later

dart

tried

Letter b is created by starting at the top, like a letter h. We then come down, up and over, completing the letter with a bowl shape.

Practise writing the letter b.

b

Now try joining a letter a to a letter b. Notice that the b is taller than the a because letter b is an ascender. We are not going to join <u>from</u> a letter b yet.

ab

abba

Letter k is also formed from the top like a letter l. When we reach the line, we move upwards just as we would for a letter b. We go up and over, but then turn in sharply to make a loop which meets the stick. We then slope downwards, before finishing with an upstroke:

Practise writing the letter k.

k

Practice Sheet 19: Practising with letters b and k

Try writing the word 'bake' in joined writing.
The letters a and e should be exactly the same height. The ascending letters b and k should be the same height as each other and clearly taller than the letters a and e.

Look at the heights.

bake

bake

book

Practise each of the words below.

make

take

table

broken

Practise writing this short sentence. Write it several times, trying to get faster but keeping your writing very tidy.

She has broken the table

TIME CHALLENGE
Time yourself for thirty seconds . Write the word 'bark' as many times as you can but keep it tidy! You should be able to write the word 'bark', neatly, about ten times.

bark

Letter p is very similar to a letter b. We start at the top of the stick, draw down through the line, draw up the same line, then loop over to make the bowl.

Practise writing the letter p.

pp

Try writing the word 'peach' in joined writing. At this stage we are not joining from the letter p yet.

The letters e, a and c should be exactly the same height. The ascending letter h should be taller than e, a and c but notice that the 'lump' on the h is the same height as these letters. The 'stick' of the letter p must go down through the line and the 'bowl' of the letter p should be the same height as the letters e, a and c.

peach

peach
peach

Practise each of the words below.

lamp

dip

apple

Now is a good time to practise joining from top joiners, like letters o and r, to a letter e:

Practise the oe and re joins.

oe oe

re re

tomatoes

Practise the word tomatoes.

tomatoes

Now practise these words, which include joining to a letter e from a top joiner:

rear

toes

reason

potatoes

TIME CHALLENGE
Time yourself writing the word 'potatoes'. Keeping your writing tidy, how long does it take you to write 'potatoes' ten times?

potatoes

Practice Sheet 22: Introducing letter f

Letter f is a very unusual letter because it is both an ascender and a descender. Not only that, its cross-line is drawn straight after drawing its basic shape rather than at the end of a word as we would with the letter t. This cross-line can then be used to join to the next letter - because of its height, the cross-line creates a join like a top joiner such as letter o or letter r.

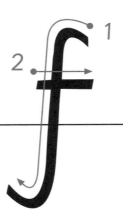

Practise the letter f.

ff

Look at the joins from a letter f to the other letters:

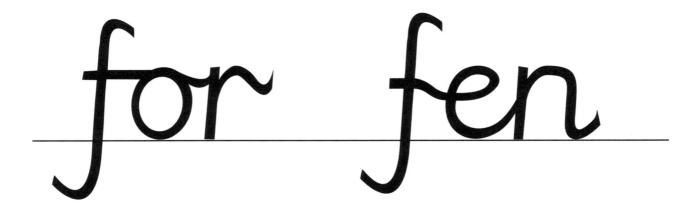

Practise these words.

for

fen

© Andrew Brodie Publications www.acblack.com

Try writing the word 'friend' in joined writing.
The letters *f* and *d* should be the same height but, of course, the letter *f* continues below the line. The letters r, i, e and n should be the same height as the bowl of the d.

friend

friend

friend

Practise each of the words below.

fridge

first

if

life

Now practise these words, which include joining to a letter e as well as some doubles:

fern

from

office

felt

TIME CHALLENGE
How many times can you write the word 'certificate' in one minute, while keeping your writing neat?

certificate

So many people have trouble with the letter j. It is actually a very simple letter to draw. These are the rules for a letter j:

Start at the top of the letter, making sure that the top is the same height as a letter a.
Draw down through the line, finishing with an 'umbrella handle' tail, like a letter g.
Draw the dot in afterwards.

Practise the letter j.

Now look at the formation of a letter y:

Practise the letter y.

Look carefully at the relative sizes of the letters in the word 'jelly':

jelly

Practise writing jelly.

jelly jelly

© Andrew Brodie Publications   www.acblack.com

Practise writing the word jammy. Try the large version first.

jammy

jammy

jammy

Notice that when you write the word 'jammy' on the lower line, the ascenders may crash into the descenders from the line above. To avoid this you need to position the words on the lower line to miss the descenders from above. Now practise these words:

hay

play

pyjamas

Now try the same words again, without the extra guideline.
Can you keep your writing tidy?

hay

play

pyjamas

Practise writing the sentence below several times. Concentrate on the sizes of the letters, making sure that your ascenders are high enough and that your descenders are low enough. After writing the sentence on the lines provided, try writing it at the bottom of the page without lines at all. Can you keep your writing tidy?

They eat jam in their pyjamas.

We have already practised letter q but we have not been able to use it within any words because we haven't yet looked at letter u.

Letter u is quite a straightforward letter to deal with. Letters before it join on to it easily and it is also easy to join from it because of its upstroke:

Practise writing the word shout.

shout

Letter q is always followed by a letter u.

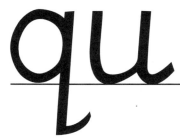

Practise writing these words with qu.

quick

quite

quiet

quad

Practise writing q and u together.

qu

qu
quietly
antiques
quiz

Practise each of these words:

under
umbrella
tune
lunch
summer

Practise writing the two sentences below. Notice that the capital letter s is as tall as the ascenders like h and l.

Shelter under the umbrella.

She hums her tunes quite quietly.

Letters v and w are extremely similar to each other:

v   w

Practise each letter.

v

w

Practise the two words 'give' and 'away'.

give

away

give away

Now look at the formation of the capital versions:

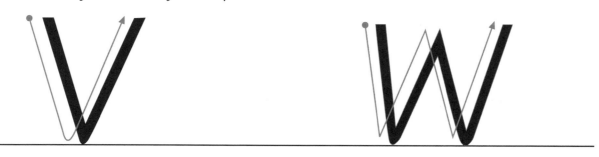

Practise writing the word 'with'. Remember to complete the word before returning to put the dot on the letter i and to put the cross on the letter t.

with

with

with

Practise each of the words below.

very

every

weave

weaving

wave

waving

Write the sentence below several times. Try to get faster each time you write the sentence but make sure you keep your writing tidy. Take particular care to keep your letters the correct size. Make sure that the ascenders are tall enough and that the descenders go far enough below the line.

We were weaving with paper.

TIME CHALLENGE
Time yourself writing the sentence below. How quickly can you write it while keeping your writing tidy? Make a second attempt to see if you can get any faster.

Welcome every member of the class.

Letters x and z are unlike any other letters.
Letter x is made by drawing two separate lines.
We can join to the letter x but we can't join from it.

Letter z is formed by one continous line:

 amaze

You can join **to** a letter z from a preceding letter, such as the letter a in the word 'amaze'.
We do not to join **from** the letter z yet.
Practise the letters and then the words.

x _____

z _____

exit _____

amaze _____

zebra _____

The capital versions of letters x and z are simply larger versions of the lower case letters:

X   Z

Practise writing the word 'excited'. Remember to join the letter x from the e but do not join the x to the c. Make sure that you keep the two parts of the word close together so that it does not look like two words: excited not ex cited.

excited

excited

excited

Practise each of the words below.

box

fix

hazy

crazy

Write the sentence below several times. Try to get faster each time you write the sentence but make sure you keep your writing tidy. Our sentence takes up a full length of the line - yours may take more than a whole line.

There was amazing excitement over the craziness of the zebra.

TIME CHALLENGE
Time yourself writing the sentence below. How quickly can you write it while keeping your writing tidy? Make a second attempt to see if you can get any faster.

The fox left the zoo through the main exit.

We have already practised some of the capital letters. Look carefully at the formation of the capital letters before practising them.
Look at the structure of the capital letters.

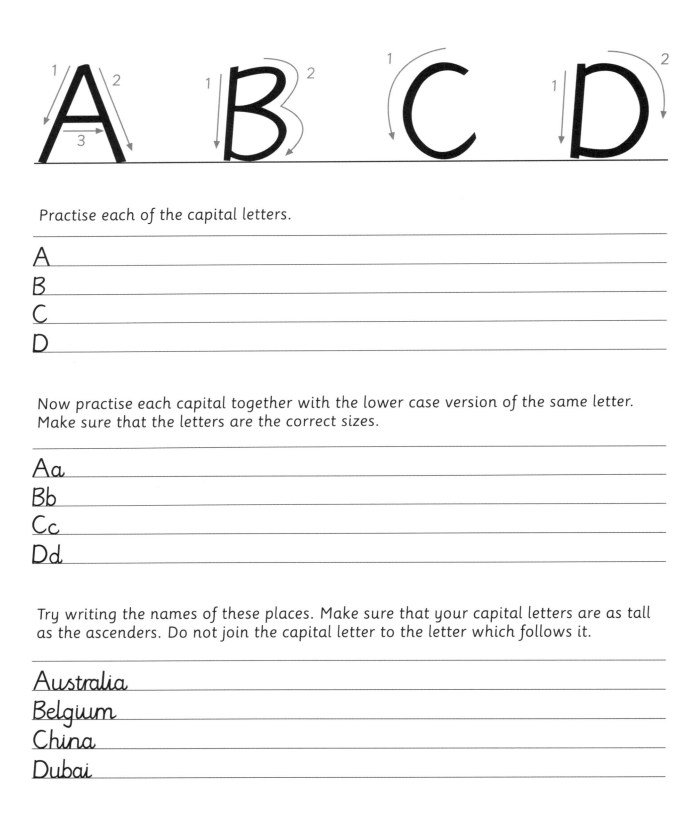

Practise each of the capital letters.

A

B

C

D

Now practise each capital together with the lower case version of the same letter.
Make sure that the letters are the correct sizes.

Aa

Bb

Cc

Dd

Try writing the names of these places. Make sure that your capital letters are as tall as the ascenders. Do not join the capital letter to the letter which follows it.

Australia

Belgium

China

Dubai

We have already practised some of the capital letters. Look carefully at the formation of the capital letters before practising them.
Look at the structure of the capital letters.

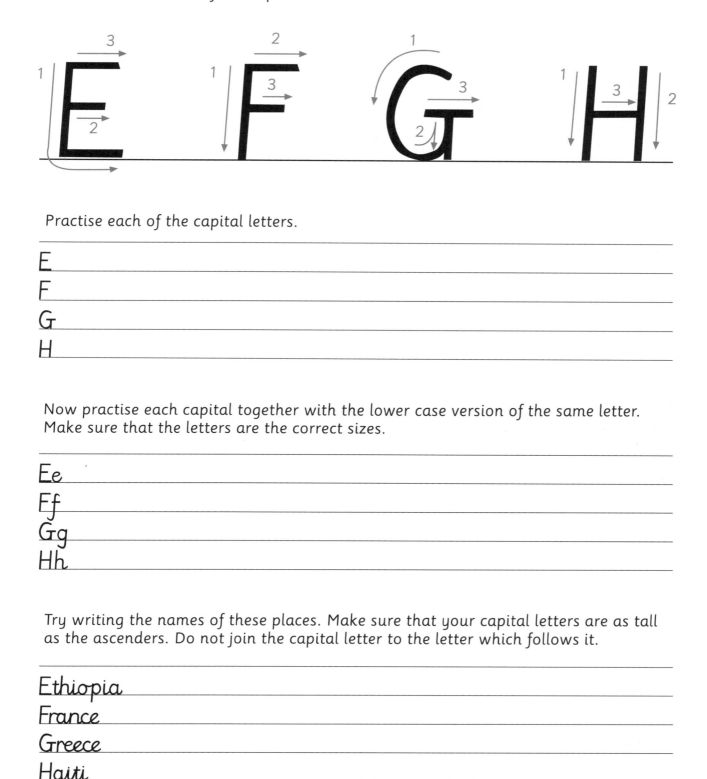

Practise each of the capital letters.

E _____

F _____

G _____

H _____

Now practise each capital together with the lower case version of the same letter. Make sure that the letters are the correct sizes.

Ee _____

Ff _____

Gg _____

Hh _____

Try writing the names of these places. Make sure that your capital letters are as tall as the ascenders. Do not join the capital letter to the letter which follows it.

Ethiopia _____

France _____

Greece _____

Haiti _____

We have already practised some of the capital letters. Look carefully at the formation of the capital letters before practising them.
Look at the structure of the capital letters.

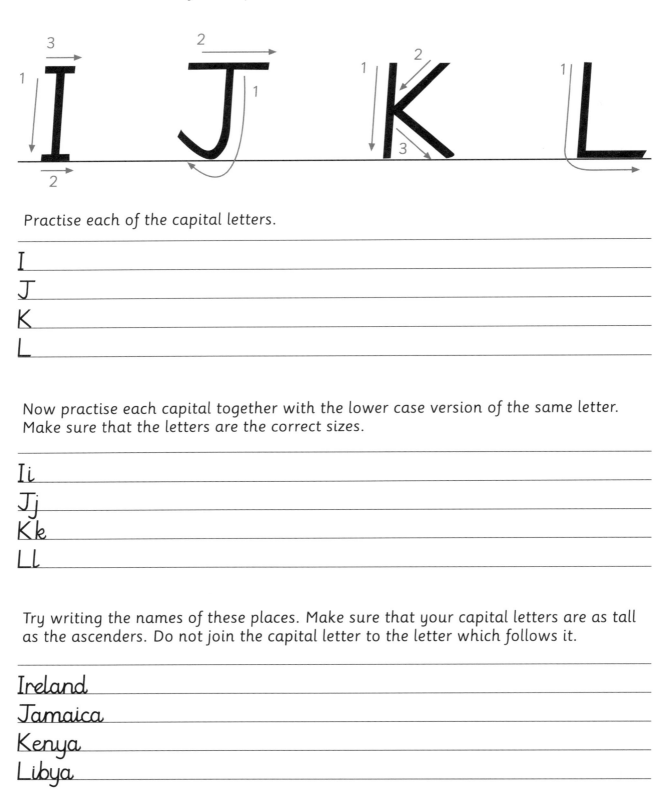

Practise each of the capital letters.

I

J

K

L

Now practise each capital together with the lower case version of the same letter. Make sure that the letters are the correct sizes.

Ii

Jj

Kk

Ll

Try writing the names of these places. Make sure that your capital letters are as tall as the ascenders. Do not join the capital letter to the letter which follows it.

Ireland

Jamaica

Kenya

Libya

We have already practised some of the capital letters. Look carefully at the formation of the capital letters before practising them.

Look at the structure of the capital letters.

Practise each of the capital letters.

M

N

O

P

Now practise each capital together with the lower case version of the same letter. Make sure that the letters are the correct sizes.

Mm

Nn

Oo

Pp

Try writing the names of these places. Make sure that your capital letters are as tall as the ascenders. Do not join the capital letter to the letter which follows it.

Mexico

Norway

Oman

Pakistan

We have already practised some of the capital letters. Look carefully at the formation of the capital letters before practising them.
Look at the structure of the capital letters.

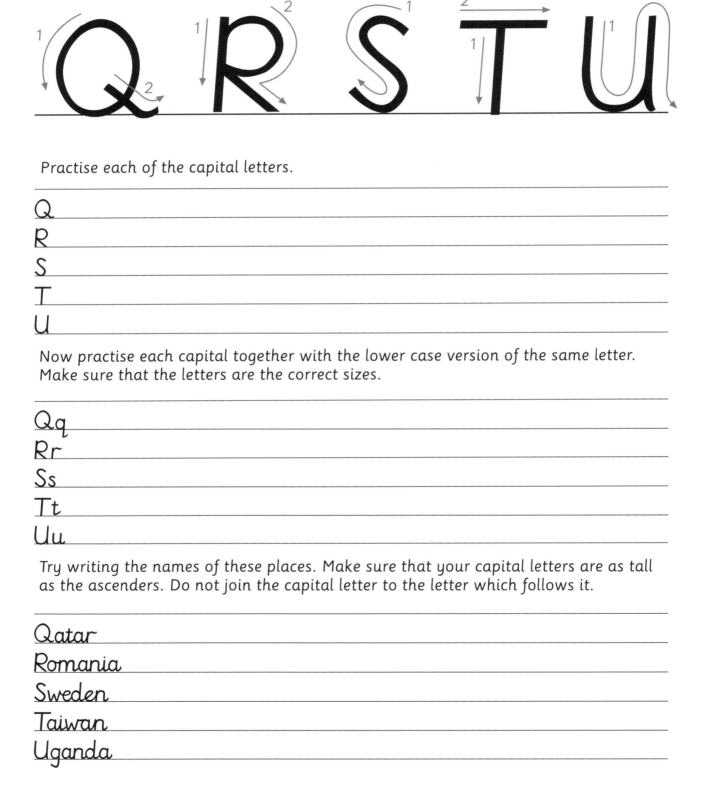

Practise each of the capital letters.

Q

R

S

T

U

Now practise each capital together with the lower case version of the same letter.
Make sure that the letters are the correct sizes.

Qq

Rr

Ss

Tt

Uu

Try writing the names of these places. Make sure that your capital letters are as tall as the ascenders. Do not join the capital letter to the letter which follows it.

Qatar

Romania

Sweden

Taiwan

Uganda

We have already practised some of the capital letters. Look carefully at the formation of the capital letters before practising them.
Look at the structure of the capital letters.

V W X Y Z

Practise each of the capital letters.

V

W

X

Y

Z

Now practise each capital together with the lower case version of the same letter. Make sure that the letters are the correct sizes.

Vv

Ww

Xx

Yy

Zz

Try writing the names of these places. Make sure that your capital letters are as tall as the ascenders. Do not join the capital letter to the letter which follows it.

Vietnam

Wales

Xian

Yemen

Zambia

Look at how we can join from a letter s.

Practise these joins.

so

see

Practise these words which include joins from letter s. Make sure that your letter s is the correct size.

sand

socks

sister

Sometimes the letter s appears several times in a word. Try these words. Remember to join every s.

assist

dresses

distress

mission

dismiss

messy

Try writing the sentence below. Make sure that every letter s is not too big.

Her dress was messy and her socks were soggy.

Look at how we can join from a letter g.

g   go

This is called a loop join.

Practise these loop joins.

go

get

Practise these words which include joins from letter g. Make sure that your letter g descends below the line.

ages

girl

sausage

Now try these words.

dogs

eggs

grit

digging

ringing

Try writing this sentence below, as neatly as you can.

He got up to go but then sat down again.

We join from a letter y using a loop join.

Practise these loop joins from a letter y.

you

yellow

Practise these words which include joins from letter y. Make sure that your loop is not too big.

yesterday

young

younger

Now try these words.

trying

crying

yoyo

your

Copy this sentence.

My yoyo is yellow, yours is green.

Joins from a letter j have a loop join.

Practise these loop joins from a letter j:

jolly

jewel

Practise these words which include joins from letter j. Make sure that your letter j goes down through the line because letter j is a descender.

jam

jar

jamjar

Now try these words:

jaw

jersey

Copy the sentence below several times. Try to make each sentence look tidy.

The jolly girl wore a yellow jersey.

Look at the join from a letter b.

Practise joining from a letter b.

bee

boy

Practise these words which include joins from a letter b. Make sure that you keep your letters the correct sizes.

badger

tube

rabbit

robot

maybe

TIME CHALLENGE
Practise writing the sentence below. Time how quickly you can write it. Keep your writing tidy, even though you are writing quickly.

The big boy began biting the banana.

Letter p joins in a similar way to letter b.

Practise joining from a letter p.

pop

pips

Practise these words which include joins from a letter p. Make sure that you keep your letters the correct sizes. Remember that p is a descender, so it goes through the line.

poppy

apple

shopping

stopped

Copy the sentence below, several times.
Try to make each sentence look better than the one before.

Put the poppies in the shopping basket.

Letter q joins to a letter u, because letter q is always
followed by letter u in English spelling.

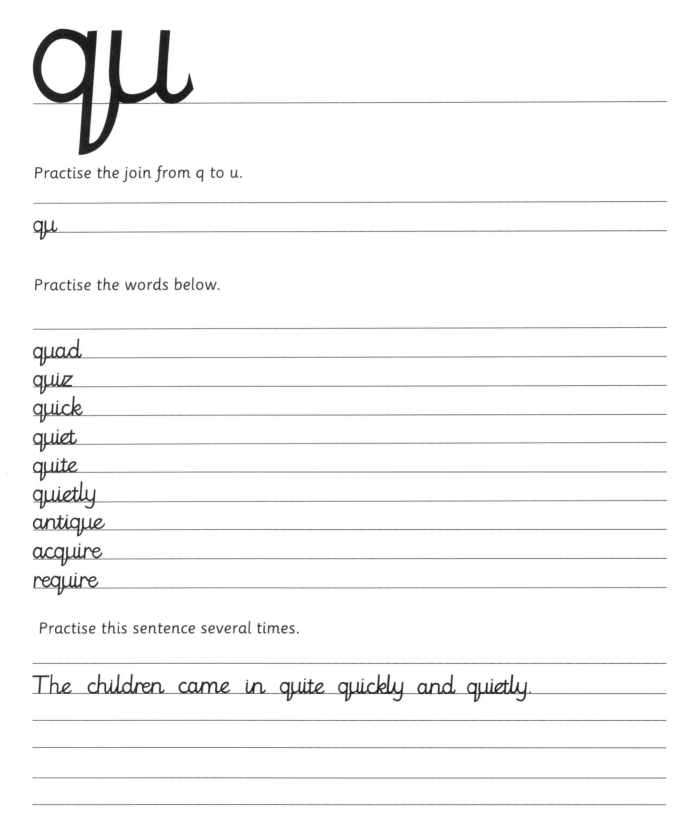

Practise the join from q to u.

qu

Practise the words below.

quad
quiz
quick
quiet
quite
quietly
antique
acquire
require

Practise this sentence several times.

The children came in quite quickly and quietly.

It is easy to join from a letter z. Just use a simple upstroke.

zoo

Practise the join from letter z.

zoo

zoology

Practise these words:

zebra

amazing

amazed

jazz

craze

crazy

craziness

laze

lazy

laziness

fizz

horizon

horizontal

haze

hazy

haziness

This is the first form of the letter x.

As you can see, we don't join from this letter x but we do join to it.

Now look at the second form of the letter x. We can write this new form of letter x without taking the pen off the paper.

With the second form of the letter x, we can join both to it and from it.

Practise writing the new type of letter x.

x

x
x
exit
exit
excited
exciting
experiment
expensive

Practice Sheet 47: Practising with letter x

Very few English words begin with the letter x.
Practise the word 'xylophone'.

xylophone

xylophone

In the words below, the letter x follows the vowel a.

axe

relaxing

In these words, the letter x follows the vowel e.

next

example

Now try words where x follows the vowel i.

six

sixty

In these words, the x follows the vowel o.

box

boxes

Here the x follows the vowel u.

luxury

deluxe

The letter f is easy to join to and from.

f   of   for

Practise writing this letter f.

f f

Now try the medium sized version.

f f

Now try the normal size, drawn in the correct position for 8mm lined paper.

Write these words.

for

off

fair

fill

far

different

© Andrew Brodie Publications   www.acblack.com

Practise writing every letter of the alphabet.

a b c d e f g h i j k l m n o p q r s t u v w x y z

Practise writing the ascenders.
Notice that the letter t is not as tall as the other ascenders.

b d f h k l t

Now practise the descenders. Notice that letter f is in this set of letters as well as the set of ascenders.

f g j p q y

Practise the letters which are neither ascenders nor descenders. Make sure that you keep them all the same size.

a c e i m n o r s u v w x z

Now practise these words which include ascenders and descenders.

fog dig buy yell key happy jet quality

Practise this sentence, which contains many letters of the alphabet:

Girls and boys should eat jelly from boxes.

Which letters of the alphabet were not included in the sentence?

Full stops: . . . .   Full stops should be written just above the level of the lower guidelines.

commas: , , , , , , , , , , , , , , , , ,   Commas can be drawn across the line. They should be very small compared to the letters.

Look.

I like carrots, peas and potatoes.

The comma crosses the line.

The full stop is just above the line.

Practise these sentences which include commas and full stops.

I like carrots, peas and potatoes.

We played tennis, football and hockey.

She wore a coat, a hat and a scarf.

We need vitamins, minerals and fibre.

One, two, three, four, five, once I caught a fish alive.

On this page we are looking at:

Speech marks: "Hello."

Notice that this full stop is written <u>before</u> the second set of speech marks.

Speech marks should be written using short, simple strokes. They should be at the same height as the tops of the ascenders. They should be very small compared to the letters.

Practise writing the word 'hello' inside speech marks.

"Hello."

Make sure: - that your speech marks curve inwards slightly.
                 - that they are about the same height as the tops of the ascenders.
                 - that the full stop is written before the final speech marks.

In the short conversation below, each sentence has a comma before the final speech marks. Practise writing the conversation.

"It is a very nice day," said Sam.
"Yes, but it is cold," replied Tariq.

Write a two line conversation of your own.

Practice Sheet 52: Using punctuation marks (3)

Quotation marks are very similar to speech marks but they are made from single strokes rather than double strokes.

Look:

'The Tempest' is by William Shakespeare.

As you can see, we use quotation marks when we are quoting the name of a play. We would also use quotation marks for the name of a book or poem.

Copy these sentences.

'The Tempest' is by William Shakespeare.

'Oliver Twist' is a book by Charles Dickens.

"I enjoyed watching 'The Tempest'," said Jasdeep.

Write a sentence which includes the name of a book you have read.

Write a sentence which includes the name of a television programme you have watched.

Apostrophes are very similar to one of the quotation marks. They should not be as high above the base-line as quotation marks or speech marks.

Look:

"Jim's dog isn't fat," said Sam.

Notice that the apostrophes in this sentence are lower than the speech marks. The apostrophes are written in the correct gaps between letters. Try practising the sentence. Write it twice.

"Jim's dog isn't fat," said Sam.

Remember, apostrophes are used for two reasons.

1. When letters are missed out.

Practise all these words.

it is → it's   can not → can't   I have → I've

I am → I'm   you are → you're   they are → they're

2. To show ownership.

Practise these sentences.

Sally's pen is blue.
Jasdeep's book is good.
I like Dave's car.
This is Tariq's house.

Question marks.

?

Copy a line of medium sized question marks.

?

Now copy some normal sized question marks. Try hard to keep them all the same size.

?

Practise writing these question words.

Why?
Where?
What?
When?
Who?
How?

Exclamation marks.

!

Copy a line of medium sized exclamation marks.

!

Now copy some normal sized exclamation marks

!
Wow!

Practice Sheet 55: Using punctuation marks (6)

Copy this piece of speech.

"Where are you going?"asked Tom.

Notice that the question mark is written <u>before</u> the closing speech marks.
Copy this piece of speech.

"I'm going to school!" shouted Lisa.

Notice that the exclamation mark is written before the closing speech marks.

Here are some other punctuation marks we sometimes use.

colons **:**   semi-colons **;**   hyphens ▬

Here is a famous line from the play 'Hamlet' by William Shakespeare.

Hamlet: To be, or not to be, - that is the question.

Notice the use of a colon and a hyphen but, although Hamlet is asking a question, Shakespeare did not use a question mark.

Copy the line from 'Hamlet' very carefully.

Hamlet: To be, or not to be, - that is the question.

Find another famous quote from 'Hamlet' to copy.

Look at how each numeral is made.

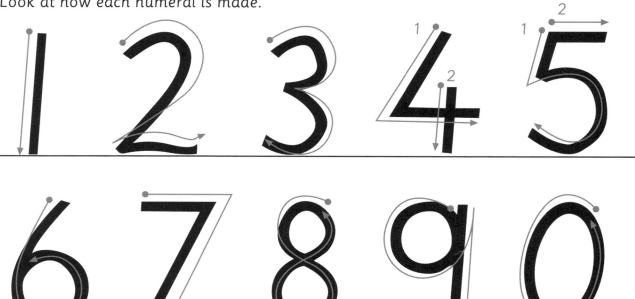

Write a row of each numeral. Try to keep each number the same size.

1

2

3

4

5

6

7

8

9

0

Practise each of these numbers.

25   162   17   500

199   384   1750

6 + 2 = 8   4 × 7 = 28

80 − 45 = 35   81 ÷ 9 = 9

Many people find the pound sign difficult to write. Try copying the pound sign.

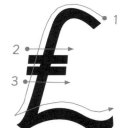

Try practising the medium sized pound sign.

Now write the pound sign in normal sized writing.

£

Copy these sums of money in numerals and words.

£500   five hundred pounds

£3.65   three pounds, sixty-five pence

£1000000   one million pounds

£8972

eight thousand, nine hundred and seventy-two pounds

£14.32   fourteen pounds, thirty-two pence

Practice Sheet 58: Developing a sloping style

Some people like to develop their writing style by sloping their letters. This can look very good if the slope is not too much.

Practise writing each capital letter, together with the lower case version of the same letter. Work slowly and carefully to try to keep your letters consistent in size and in slope.

Aa

Bb

Cc

Dd

Ee

Ff

Gg

Hh

Ii

Jj

Kk

Ll

Mm

Nn

Oo

Pp

Qq

Rr

Ss

Tt

Uu

Vv

Ww

Xx

Yy

Zz

Look again at the famous quote from Shakespeare's 'Hamlet, Prince of Denmark':

To be, or not to be, - that is the question.

Now look at the same quote, this time with a slope:

To be, or not to be, - that is the question.

Which do you prefer to look at?

Try writing the quote using a gentle slope.

To be, or not to be, - that is the question.

Now try some other quotes from Shakespeare.

A horse! a horse! my kingdom for a horse!

Let's to billiards.

Not a mouse stirring.

He hath eaten me out of house and home.

I am too old to learn.

What's mine is yours, and what is yours is mine.

Practise writing these imaginary addresses on the envelopes shown.

The Managing Director
FCSA Trading Company
Rumdonald
Scotland
RU6 9ZT

Miss Sophie Harrison
28 Claystoke Road
Alvercreek
Dorset
TO7 8ME

Now try writing your own address and the address of a friend.

Use your best handwriting to practise writing these facts about our solar system.

Mercury is the closest planet to the sun.

The planet furthest from the sun is Pluto.

Earth is 150 million kilometres from the sun.

The largest planet in our solar system is Jupiter.

The second largest planet is Saturn.

Venus, Mars, Neptune and Uranus are also planets.

There are nine planets which travel around the sun.

Practice Sheet 62: Practising the slope (4)

Try writing the names of these places using sloping joined writing. Remember to make sure that your capital letters are as tall as the ascenders. Remember not to join the capital letter to the letter which follows it.

Amsterdam

Brussels

Cardiff

Dundee

Edinburgh

Florence

Geneva

Helsinki

Innsbruck

Jakarta

Kuala Lumpur

Lisbon

Manchester

Naples

Oslo

Prague

Quebec

Reykjavik

Southampton

Tripoli

Ullapool

Vancouver

Wellington

Xai-Xai

Yarmouth

Zap

Practise this piece of writing using sloping handwriting.

Be careful with the speech marks and the other punctuation marks.

"My pen's run out!" shouted my sister.

"Go and fetch it then," I said.

"The computer's gone down," said my dad.

"Down where?" I enquired.

"The car's up the creek," moaned mum.

"Which creek's that?" I asked.

"You're for the high jump!" they all yelled.

So I closed my mouth tightly,

and didn't say a word.

Here is a letter from a boy to his friend. You can copy the letter for handwriting practise or write a letter of your own to one of your friends.

28, Claystoke Road
Alvercreek
Dorset
TO 78 ME

Tuesday 27th October

Dear Tariq,

Thanks very much for sending my birthday present. Some of the stitching was going on my old leather football so I'm really pleased to have a new one.

Sorry you couldn't come out bowling with us. It was good fun.

See you at school next week.

From Tom.

Practice Sheet 65: Informal letter template

Write your own address here.

_____

_____

Use paper-clips to fasten a piece of paper
to this template. You should be able to
see the lines through your paper.

_____

_____

_____

_____

Write the date here.
_____

Dear ......
_____

Most people like to start with an indent
from the edge of the writing area.
_____

_____

_____

_____

_____

_____

_____

_____

_____

_____

_____

If you need to write a formal letter you may wish to use a computer or you may choose to use handwriting. Here is an imaginary formal letter written by hand:

The Manager
Big Ten Bowling
High Farm Park
Alvercreek
Dorset
TO6 4ZT

28, Claystoke Road
Alvercreek
Dorset
TO7 8ME

19th October 2001

Dear Sir or Madam,

I would like to book two lanes for ten pin bowling on Monday 26th October. I am hoping to bring a group of twelve boys and girls at about 4pm. Please let me know if this will be possible. I would be grateful if you could also confirm the cost.
Thank you for your help.

Yours faithfully,

Sophie Harrison.

You can copy the letter for handwriting practise or write an imaginary formal letter of your own.

Practice Sheet 67: Formal letter template

Write your own address here.

_____

_____

_____

_____

Write the address of the recipient here so
_____
that it will appear through the window
_____
of a standard window envelope.
_____

_____

_____

Write the date here.
_____

Dear Sir or Madam (or you can use the recipient's name if you know it)
_____
We can start writing from the edge of our writing area
as business letters often don't have an indent.
_____

_____

_____

_____

_____

_____

_____

When ending a formal letter you should write...
_____

_____

Yours faithfully,   if you have written Dear Sir or Madam.
_____

Yours sincerely,   if you have used the recipient's name.
_____

_____

You have now learnt basic letter formations and joins to enable you to write tidily and quickly. You have practised sloping your writing and you are now ready to make further developments to your own style. There are a few simple rules which you will need to apply at any time that you are writing:

Make sure that you are sitting comfortably, that your desk is not cluttered, that you have good light to work by and that you are holding your paper still.

Choose a pen which you are comfortable with and hold it correctly.

Be very careful to keep your letters the right size:

a c e i m n o r s u v w x z

b d f h k l t

f g j p q y

Now look at all the letters together, comparing their sizes:

a b c d e f g h i j k l m n o p q r s t u v w x y z

Be careful to keep a clear gap between your words …

I went for a walk today.

… but don't make the gaps too wide!

I went for a walk today

You may like to write on plain paper instead of lined paper and, for this, you may find line-guides helpful. You can fasten your A4 size paper to the line-guide using paper-clips.

Enjoy your writing.